Joint FAO/WHO Food Standa
CODEX ALIMENTARIUS C

CU00406139

CODEX ALIMENTARIUS

**FOOD LABELLING
COMPLETE TEXTS**

FOOD AND AGRICULTURE ORGANIZATION
OF THE UNITED NATIONS
WORLD HEALTH ORGANIZATION
Rome, 1998

M-83

ISBN 92-5-104142-3

PREFACE

THE CODEX ALIMENTARIUS COMMISSION AND THE FAO/WHO FOOD STANDARDS PROGRAMME

The Codex Alimentarius Commission implements the Joint FAO/WHO Food Standards Programme, the purpose of which is to protect the health of consumers and to ensure fair practices in the food trade. The *Codex Alimentarius* (Latin, meaning Food Law or Code) is a collection of internationally adopted food standards presented in a uniform manner. It also includes provisions of an advisory nature in the form of codes of practice, guidelines and other recommended measures to assist in achieving the purposes of the Codex Alimentarius. The Commission has expressed the view that codes of practice might provide useful checklists of requirements for national food control or enforcement authorities. The publication of the Codex Alimentarius is intended to guide and promote the elaboration and establishment of definitions and requirements for foods, to assist in their harmonization and, in doing so, to facilitate international trade.

FOOD LABELLING - COMPLETE TEXTS

Food labelling is the primary means of communication between the producer and seller of food on one hand, and the purchaser and consumer of the other. The Codex Alimentarius standards and guidelines on food labelling published in various volumes of the *Codex Alimentarius* are now collected and republished in this compact format to allow their wide use and understanding by governments, regulatory authorities, food industries and retailers, and consumers.

Further information on these texts, or any other aspect of the Codex Alimentarius Commission, may be obtained from:

> *The Secretary,*
> *Codex Alimentarius Commission,*
> *Joint FAO/WHO Food Standards Programme,*
> *FAO, Viale delle Terme di Caracalla,*
> *00100, Rome Italy*
>
> *fax: +39(6)57.05.45.93*
> *email: codex@fao.org*

CONTENTS

CODEX GENERAL STANDARD FOR THE LABELLING OF PREPACKAGED FOODS

CODEX STAN 1-1985 (Rev. 1-1991)[1]

1.   SCOPE

This standard applies to the labelling of all prepackaged foods to be offered as such to the consumer or for catering purposes and to certain aspects relating to the presentation thereof.[2]

2.   DEFINITION OF TERMS

For the purpose of this standard:

"Claim" means any representation which states, suggests or implies that a food has particular qualities relating to its origin, nutritional properties, nature, processing, composition or any other quality.

"Consumer" means persons and families purchasing and receiving food in order to meet their personal needs.

"Container" means any packaging of food for delivery as a single item, whether by completely or partially enclosing the food and includes wrappers.   A container may enclose several units or types of packages when such is offered to the consumer.

For use in **Date Marking** of prepackaged food:

---

[1]   The Codex General Standard for the Labelling of Prepackaged Foods was adopted by the Codex Alimentarius Commission at its 14th Session, 1981 and subsequently revised in 1985 and 1991 by the 16th and 19th Sessions. This standard has been submitted to all Member Nations and Associate Members of FAO and WHO for acceptance in accordance with the General Principles of the Codex Alimentarius.

[2]   When notifying their position on the acceptance of this standard, governments are requested to indicate any provisions concerning the presentation of mandatory information on the label and in labelling, in force in their country which are not covered by this standard.

"Date of Manufacture" means the date on which the food becomes the product as described.

"Date of Packaging" means the date on which the food is placed in the immediate container in which it will be ultimately sold.

"Sell-by-Date" means the last date of offer for sale to the consumer after which there remains a reasonable storage period in the home.

"Date of Minimum Durability" ("best before") means the date which signifies the end of the period under any stated storage conditions during which the product will remain fully marketable and will retain any specific qualities for which tacit or express claims have been made. However, beyond the date the food may still be perfectly satisfactory.

"Use-by Date" (Recommended Last Consumption Date, Expiration Date) means the date which signifies the end of the estimated period under any stated storage conditions, after which the product probably will not have the quality attributes normally expected by the consumers. After this date, the food should not be regarded as marketable.

"Food" means any substance, whether processed, semi-processed or raw, which is intended for human consumption, and includes drinks, chewing gum and any substance which has been used in the manufacture, preparation or treatment of "food" but does not include cosmetics or tobacco or substances used only as drugs.

"Food Additive" means any substance not normally consumed as a food by itself and not normally used as a typical ingredient of the food, whether or not it has nutritive value, the intentional addition of which to food for a technological (including organoleptic) purpose in the manufacture, processing, preparation, treatment, packing, packaging, transport or holding of such food results, or may be reasonably expected to result, (directly or indirectly) in it or its by-products becoming a component of or otherwise affecting the characteristics of such foods. The term does not include "contaminants" or substances added to food for maintaining or improving nutritional qualities.

"Ingredient" means any substance, including a food additive, used in the manufacture or preparation of a food and present in the final product although possibly in a modified form.

"**Label**" means any tag, brand, mark, pictorial or other descriptive matter, written, printed, stencilled, marked, embossed or impressed on, or attached to, a container of food.

"**Labelling**" includes any written, printed or graphic matter that is present on the label, accompanies the food, or is displayed near the food, including that for the purpose of promoting its sale or disposal.

"**Lot**" means a definitive quantity of a commodity produced essentially under the same conditions.

"**Prepackaged**" means packaged or made up in advance in a container, ready for offer to the consumer, or for catering purposes.

"**Processing Aid**" means a substance or material, not including apparatus or utensils, and not consumed as a food ingredient by itself, intentionally used in the processing of raw materials, foods or its ingredients, to fulfil a certain technological purpose during treatment or processing and which may result in the non-intentional but unavoidable presence of residues or derivatives in the final product.

"**Foods for Catering Purposes**" means those foods for use in restaurants, canteens, schools, hospitals and similar institutions where food is offered for immediate consumption.

3.   GENERAL PRINCIPLES

3.1   Prepackaged food shall not be described or presented on any label or in any labelling in a manner that is false, misleading or deceptive or is likely to create an erroneous impression regarding its character in any respect.[1]

3.2   Prepackaged food shall not be described or presented on any label or in any labelling by words, pictorial or other devices which refer to or are suggestive either directly or indirectly, of any other product with which such food might be confused, or in such a manner as to lead the purchaser or consumer to suppose that the food is connected with such other product.

---

[1]   Examples of descriptions or presentations to which these General Principles refer are given in the Codex General Guidelines on Claims.

4. MANDATORY LABELLING OF PREPACKAGED FOODS

The following information shall appear on the label of prepackaged foods as applicable to the food being labelled, except to the extent otherwise expressly provided in an individual Codex standard:

4.1 THE NAME OF THE FOOD

4.1.1 The name shall indicate the true nature of the food and normally be specific and not generic:

4.1.1.1 Where a name or names have been established for a food in a Codex standard, at least one of these names shall be used.

4.1.1.2 In other cases, the name prescribed by national legislation shall be used.

4.1.1.3 In the absence of any such name, either a common or usual name existing by common usage as an appropriate descriptive term which was not misleading or confusing to the consumer shall be used.

4.1.1.4 A "coined", "fanciful", "brand" name, or "trade mark" may be used provided it accompanies one of the names provided in Subsections 4.1.1.1 to 4.1.1.3.

4.1.2 There shall appear on the label either in conjunction with, or in close proximity to, the name of the food, such additional words or phrases as necessary to avoid misleading or confusing the consumer in regard to the true nature and physical condition of the food including but not limited to the type of packing medium, style, and the condition or type of treatment it has undergone; for example: dried, concentrated, reconstituted, smoked.

4.2 LIST OF INGREDIENTS

4.2.1 Except for single ingredient foods, a list of ingredients shall be declared on the label.

4.2.1.1 The list of ingredients shall be headed or preceded by an appropriate title which consists of or includes the term 'ingredient'.

4.2.1.2 All ingredients shall be listed in descending order of ingoing weight (m/m) at the time of the manufacture of the food.

4.2.1.3 Where an ingredient is itself the product of two or more ingredients, such a compound ingredient may be declared, as such, in the list of ingredients provided that it is immediately accompanied by a list in brackets of its ingredients in descending order of proportion (m/m). Where a compound ingredient for which a name has been established in a Codex standard or in national legislation constitutes less than 25% of the food, the ingredients other than food additives which serve a technological function in the finished product need not be declared.

4.2.1.4 Added water shall be declared in the list of ingredients except when the water forms part of an ingredient such as brine, syrup or broth used in a compound food and declared as such in the list of ingredients. Water or other volatile ingredients evaporated in the course of manufacture need not be declared.

4.2.1.5 As an alternative to the general provisions of this section, dehydrated or condensed foods which are intended to be reconstituted by the addition of water only, the ingredients may be listed in order of proportion (m/m) in the reconstituted product provided that a statement such as "ingredients of the product when prepared in accordance with the directions on the label" is included.

4.2.2 A specific name shall be used for ingredients in the list of ingredients in accordance with the provisions set out in Section 4.1 (Name of the Food) except that:

4.2.2.1 The following class names may be used for the ingredients falling within these classes:

NAME OF CLASSES	CLASS NAMES
Refined oils other than olive	'Oil' together with either the term 'vegetable' or 'animal', qualified by the term 'hydrogenated' or 'partially-hydrogenated', as appropriate
Refined fats	'Fat' together with either, the term 'vegetable' or 'animal', as appropriate.
Starches, other than chemically	'Starch'.

modified starches

All species of fish where the fish constitutes an ingredient of another food and provided that the labelling and presentation of such food does not refer to a specific species of fish.	'Fish'.
All types of poultrymeat where such meat constitutes an ingredient of another food and provided that the labelling and presentation of such a food does not refer to a specific type of poultrymeat.	'Poultrymeat'.
All types of cheese where the cheese or mixture of cheeses constitutes an ingredient of another food and provided that the labelling and presentation of such food does not refer to a specific type of cheese	'Cheese'
All spices and spice extracts not exceeding 2% by weight either singly or in combination in the food.	'Spice', 'spices', or 'mixed spices', as appropriate.
All herbs or parts of herbs not exceeding 2% by weight either singly or in combination in the food	'Herbs' or 'mixed herbs', as appropriate.
All types of gum preparations used in the manufacture of gum base for chewing gum.	'Gum base'.
All types of sucrose.	'Sugar'.
Anhydrous dextrose and dextrose monohydrate	'Dextrose' or 'glucose'.
All types of caseinates.	'Caseinates'.
Press, expeller or refined cocoa butter.	'Cocoa butter'.

| All crystallized fruit not exceeding 10% of the weight of the food. | 'Crystallized fruit'. |

4.2.2.2Notwithstanding the provision set out in Section 4.2.2.1, pork fat, lard and beef fat shall always be declared by their specific names.

4.2.2.3For food additives falling in the respective classes and appearing in lists of food additives permitted for use in foods generally, the following class titles shall be used together with the specific name or recognized numerical identification as required by national legislation.[1]

- Acidity Regulator
- Acids
- Anticaking Agent
- Antifoaming Agent
- Antioxidant
- Bulking Agent
- Colour
- Colour Retention Agent
- Emulsifier
- Emulsifying Salt
- Firming Agent

- Flour Treatment Agent
- Flavour Enhancer
- Gelling Agent
- Glazing Agent
- Humectant
- Preservative
- Propellant
- Raising Agent
- Stabilizer
- Sweetener
- Thickener

---

[1]   Governments accepting the standard should indicate the requirements in force in their countries.

4.2.2.4 The following class titles may be used for food additives falling in the respective classes and appearing in lists of food additives permitted generally for use in foods:

- Flavour(s) and Flavouring(s)
- Modified Starch(es)

The expression "flavours" may be qualified by "natural", "nature identical", "artificial" or a combination of these words as appropriate.

4.2.3 *Processing Aids and Carry-Over of Food Additives*

4.2.3.1 A food additive carried over into a food in a significant quantity or in an amount sufficient to perform a technological function in that food as a result of the use of raw materials or other ingredients in which the additive was used shall be included in the list of ingredients.

4.2.3.2 A food additive carried over into foods at a level less than that required to achieve a technological function, and processing aids, are exempted from declaration in the list of ingredients.

4.3   NET CONTENTS AND DRAINED WEIGHT

4.3.1 The net contents shall be declared in the metric system ("Système International" units).[1]

4.3.2 The net contents shall be declared in the following manner:

(i)   for liquid foods, by volume;

(ii)   for solid foods, by weight;

(iii) for semi-solid or viscous foods, either by weight or volume.

4.3.3 In addition to the declaration of net contents, a food packed in a liquid medium shall carry a declaration in the metric system of the drained weight of the food. For the purposes of this requirement, liquid medium means water,

---

[1]   The declaration of net contents represents the quantity at the time of packaging and is subject to enforcement by reference to an average system of quantity control.

aqueous solutions of sugar and salt, fruit and vegetable juices in canned fruits and vegetables only, or vinegar, either singly or in combination.[1]

4.4   NAME AND ADDRESS

The name and address of the manufacturer, packer, distributor, importer, exporter or vendor of the food shall be declared.

4.5   COUNTRY OF ORIGIN

4.5.1   The country of origin of the food shall be declared if its omission would mislead or deceive the consumer.

4.5.2   When a food undergoes processing in a second country which changes its nature, the country in which the processing is performed shall be considered to be the country of origin for the purposes of labelling.

4.6   LOT IDENTIFICATION

Each container shall be embossed or otherwise permanently marked in code or in clear to identify the producing factory and the lot.

4.7   DATE MARKING AND STORAGE INSTRUCTIONS

4.7.1   If not otherwise determined in an individual Codex standard, the following date marking shall apply:

   (i)   The "date of minimum durability" shall be declared.

   (ii)   This shall consist at least of:

   - the day and the month for products with a minimum durability of not more than three months;

   - the month and the year for products with a minimum durability of more than three months.   If the month is December, it is sufficient to indicate the year.

   (iii) The date shall be declared by the words:

---

[1]   The declaration of drained weight is subject to enforcement by reference to an average system of quantity control.

- "Best before ..." where the day is indicated;

- "Best before end ..." in other cases.

(iv) The words referred to in paragraph (iii) shall be accompanied by:

- either the date itself; or

- a reference to where the date is given.

(v) The day, month and year shall be declared in uncoded numerical sequence except that the month may be indicated by letters in those countries where such use will not confuse the consumer.

(vi) Notwithstanding 4.7.1 (i) an indication of the date of minimum durability shall not be required for:

- fresh fruits and vegetables, including potatoes which have not been peeled, cut or similarly treated;

- wines, liqueur wines, sparkling wines, aromatized wines, fruit wines and sparkling fruit wines;

- beverages containing 10% or more by volume of alcohol;

- bakers' or pastry-cooks' wares which, given the nature of their content, are normally consumed within 24 hours of their manufacture;

- vinegar;

- food grade salt;

- solid sugars;

- confectionery products consisting of flavoured and/or coloured sugars;

- chewing gum.

4.7.2 In addition to the date of minimum durability, any special conditions for the storage of the food shall be declared on the label if the validity of the date depends thereon.

4.8   INSTRUCTIONS FOR USE

Instructions for use, including reconstitution, where applicable, shall be included on the label, as necessary, to ensure correct utilization of the food.

5.   *ADDITIONAL MANDATORY REQUIREMENTS*

5.1   QUANTITATIVE LABELLING OF INGREDIENTS

5.1.1   Where the labelling of a food places special emphasis on the presence of one or more valuable and/or characterizing ingredients, or where the description of the food has the same effect, the ingoing percentage of the ingredient (m/m) at the time of manufacture shall be declared.

5.1.2   Similarly, where the labelling of a food places special emphasis on the low content of one or more ingredients, the percentage of the ingredient (m/m) in the final product shall be declared.

5.1.3   A reference in the name of a food to a particular ingredient shall not of itself constitute the placing of special emphasis. A reference in the labelling of a food to an ingredient used in a small quantity and only as a flavouring shall not of itself constitute the placing of special emphasis.

5.2   IRRADIATED FOODS

5.2.1   The label of a food which has been treated with ionizing radiation shall carry a written statement indicating that treatment in close proximity to the name of the food. The use of the international food irradiation symbol, as shown below, is optional, but when it is used, it shall be in close proximity to the name of the food.

5.2.2   When an irradiated product is used as an ingredient in another food, this shall be so declared in the list of ingredients.

5.2.3   When a single ingredient product is prepared from a raw material which has been irradiated, the label of the product shall contain a statement indicating the treatment.

6.   EXEMPTIONS FROM MANDATORY LABELLING REQUIREMENTS

With the exception of spices and herbs, small units, where the largest surface area is less than 10 cm², may be exempted from the requirements of paragraphs 4.2 and 4.6 to 4.8.

7.   OPTIONAL LABELLING

7.1   Any information or pictorial device written, printed, or graphic matter may be displayed in labelling provided that it is not in conflict with the mandatory requirements of this standard and those relating to claims and deception given in Section 3 - General Principles.

7.2   If grade designations are used, they shall be readily understandable and not be misleading or deceptive in any way.

8.   PRESENTATION OF MANDATORY INFORMATION

8.1   GENERAL

8.1.1   Labels in prepackaged foods shall be applied in such a manner that they will not become separated from the container.

8.1.2   Statements required to appear on the label by virtue of this standard or any other Codex standards shall be clear, prominent, indelible and readily legible by the consumer under normal conditions of purchase and use.

8.1.3   Where the container is covered by a wrapper, the wrapper shall carry the necessary information or the label on the container shall be readily legible through the outer wrapper or not obscured by it.

8.1.4   The name and net contents of the food shall appear in a prominent position and in the same field of vision.

8.2   LANGUAGE

8.2.1   If the language on the original label is not acceptable, to the consumer for whom it is intended, a supplementary label containing the mandatory information in the required language may be used instead of relabelling.

8.2.2   In the case of either relabelling or a supplementary label, the mandatory information provided shall be fully and accurately reflect that in the original label.

CODEX GENERAL STANDARD FOR THE LABELLING OF FOOD ADDITIVES WHEN SOLD AS SUCH

CODEX STAN 107-1981[1]

1. SCOPE

This standard applies to the labelling of "food additives" sold as such whether by retail or other than by retail, including sales to caterers and food manufacturers for the purpose of their businesses. This standard also applies to food "processing aids"; any reference to food additives includes food processing aids.

2. DEFINITION OF TERMS

For the purpose of this standard:

(a) *food additive* means any substance not normally consumed as a food by itself and not normally used as a typical ingredient of the food, whether or not it has nutritive value, the intentional addition of which to food for a technological (including organoleptic) purpose in the manufacture, processing, preparation, treatment, packing, packaging, transport or holding of such food results, or may be reasonably expected to result, (directly or indirectly) in it or its by-products becoming a component of or otherwise affecting the characteristics of such foods. The term does not include contaminants, or substances added to food for maintaining or improving nutritional qualities, or sodium chloride;

(b) *processing aid* means a substance or material not including apparatus or utensils and not consumed as a food ingredient by itself, intentionally used in the processing of raw materials, foods or its ingredients to fulfil a certain technological purpose during treatment or processing and which may result in the non-intentional but unavoidable presence of residues or derivatives in the final product;

---

[1] The Codex General Standard for the Labelling of Food Additives When Sold as Such was adopted by the Codex Alimentarius at its 14th Session in 1981. This Standard has been submitted to all Member Nations and Associate Members of FAO and WHO for **acceptance** in accordance with the General Principles of the Codex Alimentarius.

(c)   ***contaminant*** means any substance not intentionally added to food, which is present in such food as a result of the production (including operations carried out in crop husbandry, animal husbandry and veterinary medicine), manufacture, processing, preparation, treatment, packing, packaging, transport or holding of such food or as a result of environmental contamination;

(d)   ***label*** includes any tag, brand, mark, pictorial or other descriptive matter, written, painted, stencilled, marked, embossed or impressed on, or attached to, a container;

(e)   ***labelling*** includes the label and any written, printed or graphic matter relating to and accompanying the food additives. The term does not include bills, invoices and similar material which may accompany the food additives;

(f)   ***container*** means any form of packaging of food additives for sale as a single item, whether by completely or partially enclosing the food additives, and includes wrappers;

(g)   ***ingredient*** means any substance, excluding a food additive, used in the manufacture or preparation of a food and present in the final product;

(h)   ***sale by retail*** means any sale to a person buying otherwise than for the purpose of resale but does not include a sale to caterers for the purposes of their catering business or a sale to manufacturers for the purposes of their manufacturing business.

3.   GENERAL PRINCIPLES

3.1   Food additives[1] shall not be described or presented on any label or in any labelling in a manner than is false, misleading or deceptive or is likely to create an erroneous impression regarding their character in any respect.

3.2   Food additives[1] shall not be described or presented on any label or in any labelling by words, pictorial or other devices which refer to or are suggestive, either directly or indirectly, of any other product with which such food additives might be confused, or in such a manner as to lead the purchaser or consumer to suppose that the food additive is connected with or derived from such other

---

[1]   The term includes "processing aids" as defined (see Scope).

product; provided that the term "x flavour" may be used to describe a flavour which is not derived from, but reproduces the flavour of "x".

4. *MANDATORY LABELLING OF PREPACKAGED FOOD ADDITIVES SOLD BY RETAIL*

The labels of all food additives sold by retail shall bear the information required by sub-sections 4.1 to 4.5 of this section, as applicable to the food additive[1] being labelled.

4.1 DETAILS OF THE FOOD ADDITIVE

(a)   The name of each food additive present shall be given. The name shall be specific and not generic and shall indicate the true nature of the food additive. Where a name has been established for a food additive in a Codex list of additives, that name shall be used. In other cases the common or usual name shall be listed or, where none exists, an appropriate descriptive name shall be used.

(b)   If two or more food additives are present, their names shall be given in the form of a list. The list shall be in the order of the proportion by weight which each food additive bears to the total contents of the container, the food additive present in the greatest proportion by weight being listed first. Where one or more of the food additives is subject to a quantitative limitation in a food covered by a Codex standard, the quantity or proportion of that additive may be stated. If food ingredients are part of the preparation, they shall be declared in the list of ingredients in descending order of proportion.

(c)   In the case of mixtures of flavourings, the name of each flavouring present in the mixture need not be given. The generic expression "flavour" or "flavouring" may be used, together with a true indication of the nature of the flavour. The expression "flavour" or "flavouring" may be qualified by the words "natural", "nature-identical", "artificial", or a combination of these words, as appropriate. This provision does not apply to flavour modifiers, but does apply to "herbs" and "spices", which generic expressions may be used where appropriate.

(d)   Food additives with a shelf-life not exceeding 18 months shall carry the date of minimum durability using words such as "will keep at least until ....".

(e)   The words "For Food Use" or a statement substantially similar thereto shall appear in a prominent position on the label.

4.2   INSTRUCTIONS ON KEEPING AND USE

Adequate information shall be given about the manner in which the food additive is to be kept and is to be used in food.

4.3   NET CONTENTS

The net contents shall be declared in either the metric (Système International Units) or avoirdupois or both systems of measurement as required by the country in which the food additive is sold. This declaration shall be made in the following manner:

(a)   for liquid food additives, by volume or weight;

(b)   for solid food additives, other than those sold in tablet form, by weight;

(c)   for semi-solid or viscous food additives, either by weight or volume;

(d)   for food additives sold in tablet form, by weight together with the number of tablets in the package.

4.4   NAME AND ADDRESS

The name and address of the manufacturer, packer, distributor, importer, exporter or vendor of the food additive shall be declared.

4.5   COUNTRY OF ORIGIN

(a)   The country of origin of a food additive shall be declared if its omission is likely to mislead or deceive the consumer.

(b)   When a food additive undergoes processing in a second country which changes its chemical or physical nature, the country in which the processing is performed shall be considered to be the country of origin for the purposes of labelling.

4.6   LOT IDENTIFICATION

Each container shall be marked in code or in clear to identify the producing factory and the lot.

5.   *MANDATORY LABELLING OF PREPACKAGED FOOD ADDITIVES SOLD OTHER THAN BY RETAIL*

The labels of all food additives sold other than by retail shall bear the information required by sub-sections 5.1 to 5.5 of this section, as applicable to the food additive being labelled;   except that, where the food additives in non-retail containers are solely destined for further industrial processing, the required information, other than that described in sections 5.1(a) and 5.1(d), may be given on the documents relating to the sale.

5.1   DETAILS OF THE FOOD ADDITIVE

(a)   The name of each food additive present shall be given. The name shall be specific and not generic and shall indicate the true nature of the food additive. Where a name has been established for a food additive in a Codex list of additives, that name shall be used. In other cases, the common or usual name shall be listed or, where none exists, an appropriate descriptive name shall be used.

(b)   If two or more food additives are present, their names shall be given in the form of a list. The list shall be in the order of the proportion by weight which each food additive bears to the total contents of the container, the food additive present in the greatest proportion by weight being listed first. Where one or more food additives is subject to a quantitative limitation in a food in the country in which the food additive is to be used, the quantity or proportion of that additive and/or adequate instruction to enable the compliance with the limitation shall be given. If food ingredients are part of the preparation, they shall be declared in the list of ingredients in descending order of proportion.

(c)   In the case of mixtures of flavourings, the name of each flavouring present in the mixture need not be given. The generic expression "flavour" or "flavouring" may be used together with a true indication of the nature of the flavour. The expression "flavour" or "flavouring" may be qualified by the words "natural", "nature-identical", "artificial", or a combination of these words, as appropriate. This provision does not apply to flavour modifiers, but does apply to "herbs" and "spices" which generic expressions may be used where appropriate.

(d)   Food additives with a shelf-life not exceeding 18 months shall carry the date of minimum durability using words such as "will keep at least until ...".

(e)   The words "For Food Use" or a statement substantially similar thereto shall appear in a prominent position on the label.

5.2   INSTRUCTIONS ON KEEPING AND USE

Adequate information shall be given about the manner in which the food additive is to be kept and is to be used in food. This information may be given on the label or in the documents relating to the sale.

5.3   NET CONTENTS

The net contents shall be declared in either (a) metric units or "Système International" units or (b) avoirdupois, unless both systems of measurement are specifically required by the country in which the food additive is sold.   The declaration shall be made in the following manner:

(i)   for liquid food additives, by volume or weight;

(ii)   for solid food additives, by weight;

(iii) for semi-solid or viscous food additives, either by weight or volume.

5.4   NAME AND ADDRESS

The name and address of the manufacturer, packer, distributor, importer, exporter or vendor of the food additive shall be declared.

5.5   COUNTRY OF ORIGIN

(a)   The country of origin of a food additive shall be declared if its omission is likely to mislead or deceive the user.

(b)   When a food additive undergoes processing in a second country which changes its chemical or physical nature, the country in which the processing is performed shall be considered to be the country of origin for the purposes of labelling.

5.6   LOT IDENTIFICATION

Each container shall be marked, in code or in clear, to identify the producing factory and the lot.

6. PRESENTATION OF MANDATORY INFORMATION

6.1 GENERAL

Statements required to appear on the label by virtue of this standard or any other Codex standard shall be clear, prominent and readily legible by the consumer under normal conditions of purchase nd use. Such information shall not be obscured by designs or by other written printed or graphic matter and shall be on contrasting ground to that of the backgpund. The letters in the name of the food additive shall be in a size reasonably related to the most prominent printed matter on the label. Where the container is covered by a wrapper, the wrapper shall carry the necessary information, or the labelon the container shall be readily legible through the outer wrapper or not obscred by it. In general the name and net contents of the food additive shall appar on that portion of the label normally intended to be presented to the consumerat the time of sale.

6.2 LANGUAGE

The language used for the declaration ofthe statements referred to in paragraph 6.1 shall be a language acceptable to the country in which the food additive is intended for sale. If the language on the original label is not acceptable, a supplementary label containing the mandatory informaton in an acceptable language may be used instead of relabelling.

7. ADDITIONAL OR DIFFERENT REQUIREMENTS FOR SPECIFIC FOOD ADDITIVES

7.1   Nothing in this standard shall preclude the adoption of additional or different provisions in a Codex standard, in respect of labelling, where the circumstances of a particular food additive would justify their incorporation in that standard.

7.2 IRRADIATED FOOD ADDITIVES

Food additives which have been treated with ionizing radiation, shall be so designated.

8.   *OPTIONAL LABELLING*

8.1   GENERAL

Any information or pictorial device may be displayed in labelling provided that it is not in conflict with the mandatory requirement nor would mislead or deceive the consumer in any way whatsoever in respect of the food additive.

GENERAL STANDARD FOR THE LABELLING OF AND CLAIMS FOR PREPACKAGED FOODS FOR SPECIAL DIETARY USES

CODEX STAN 146-1985[1]

1.   SCOPE

This standard applies to the labelling of all prepackaged foods for special dietary uses as defined in Section 2.1 to be offered as such to the consumer or for catering purposes and to certain aspects relating to the presentation thereof; and to claims made for such foods.

2.   DESCRIPTION

2.1   Foods for Special Dietary Uses are those foods which are specially processed or formulated to satisfy particular dietary requirements which exist because of a particular physical or physiological condition and/or specific diseases and disorders and which are presented as such[2]   The composition of these foodstuffs must differ significantly from the composition of ordinary foods of comparable nature, if such ordinary foods exist.

2.2   The definitions laid down in the Codex General Standard for the Labelling of Prepackaged Foods[3] (see page 1) apply.

3.   GENERAL PRINCIPLES

3.1   Prepackaged Foods for Special Dietary Uses shall not be described or presented in a manner that is false, misleading or deceptive or is likely to create an erroneous impression regarding their character in any respect.[4]

---

[1]   The General Standard for the Labelling of and Claims for Prepackaged Foods for Special Dietary Uses was adopted by the 16th Session of the Codex Alimentarius Commission in 1985. This standard has been submitted to all Member Nations and Associate Members of FAO and WHO for acceptance in accordance with the General Principles of the Codex Alimentarius.

[2]   This includes foods for infants and young children.

[3]   Hereafter referred to as "General Standard".

3.2   Nothing in the labelling and advertising of foods to which this standard applies shall imply that advice from a qualified person is not needed.

4.   MANDATORY LABELLING OF PREPACKAGED FOODS FOR SPECIAL DIETARY USES

The label of all prepackaged Foods for Special Dietary Uses shall bear the information required by Sections 4.1 to 4.8 of this standard as applicable to the food being labelled, except to the extent otherwise expressly provided in a specific Codex standard.

4.1   THE NAME OF THE FOOD

In addition to the declaration of the name of the food in accordance with Section 4.1 of the General Standard, the following provisions apply:

4.1.1   The designation "special dietary", "special dietetic" or an appropriate equivalent term, may be used in conjunction with the name only where the product corresponds to the definition in Section 2.1.

4.1.2   The characterizing essential feature, but not the condition for which the food is intended, shall be stated in appropriate descriptive terms in close proximity to the name of the food.

4.2   LIST OF INGREDIENTS

The declaration of the list of ingredients shall be in accordance with Section 4.2 of the General Standard.

4.3   NUTRITION LABELLING

4.3.1   The declaration of nutrition information on the label shall include the following:

(a)   The amount of energy per 100 grammes or 100 ml of the food as sold and where appropriate per specified quantity of the food as suggested for consumption, expressed in kilocalories (kcal) and kilojoules (kJ).

---

[4]   Examples of descriptions or presentations to which these General Principles refer, are given in the Codex General Guidelines on Claims (See page 29).

(b)   The number of grammes of protein, available carbohydrate and fat per 100 grammes or 100 ml of the food as sold and where appropriate per specified quantity of the food as suggested for consumption.

(c)   The total quantity of those specific nutrients or other components which provide the characterizing essential feature for the special dietary use for which the food is intended per 100 grammes or 100 ml of the food as sold and, where appropriate, per specified quantity of the food as suggested for consumption.

4.4   NET CONTENTS AND DRAINED WEIGHT

The declaration of net contents and drained weight shall be in accordance with Section 4.3 of the General Standard.

4.5   NAME AND ADDRESS

The name and address shall be declared in accordance with Section 4.4 of the General Standard.

4.6   COUNTRY OF ORIGIN

The country of origin shall be declared in accordance with Section 4.5 of the General Standard.

4.7   LOT IDENTIFICATION

The lot identification shall be declared in accordance with Section 4.6 of the General Standard.

4.8   DATE MARKING AND STORAGE INSTRUCTIONS

In addition to the declaration of date marking and storage instructions in accordance with Section 4.7 of the General Standard, the following provisions apply:

4.8.1   Storage of Opened Food

Storage instructions of opened packages of a food for special dietary uses shall be included on the label if necessary to ensure that the opened product maintains its wholesomeness and nutritive value. A warning should be included on the label if the food is not capable of being stored after opening or is not capable of being stored in the container after opening.

5. ADDITIONAL MANDATORY REQUIREMENTS FOR SPECIFIC FOODS

5.1 QUANTITATIVE LABELLING OF INGREDIENTS

The quantitative labelling of ingredients shall be in accordance with Section 5.1 of the General Standard.

5.2 CLAIMS

5.2.1 Any claims made for the foods covered by this standard shall be in accordance with the General Guidelines on Claims elaborated by the Codex Alimentarius Commission (See page 29 *et seq.*).

5.2.2 Where a claim is made that the food is suitable for "special dietary use" that food shall comply with all provisions of this standard except as otherwise provided in a specific Codex Standard for Foods for Special Dietary Uses.

5.2.3 A food which has not been modified in accordance with Section 2.1 but is suitable for use in a particular dietary regimen because of its natural composition, shall not be designated "special dietary" or "special dietetic" or any other equivalent term. However, such a food may bear a statement on the label that "this food is by its nature "X"" ("X" refers to the essential distinguishing characteristic), provided that such statement does not mislead the consumer.

5.2.4 Claims as to the suitability of a food defined in Section 2.1 for use in the prevention, alleviation, treatment or cure of a disease, disorder or particular physiological condition are prohibited unless they are:

(a) in accordance with the provisions of Codex standards or guidelines for foods for special dietary uses, and follow the principles set forth in such standards or guidelines; or

(b) in the absence of an applicable Codex standard or guideline, permitted under the laws of the country in which the food is distributed.

5.3 IRRADIATED FOODS

Irradiated foods for special dietary uses shall be labelled in accordance with Section 5.2 of the General Standard.

5.4 Nothing in this standard shall preclude the adoption of additional or different provisions in a Codex standard for a food for special dietary use, in respect of labelling, where the circumstances of a particular food would justify their incorporation in that standard.

6. EXEMPTIONS FROM MANDATORY LABELLING REQUIREMENTS

Exemptions from mandatory labelling requirements shall be in accordance with Section 6 of the General Standard.

7. OPTIONAL LABELLING

Optional labelling of foods for special dietary uses shall be in accordance with Section 7 of the General Standard.

8. PRESENTATION OF MANDATORY INFORMATION

The presentation of the mandatory information shall be in accordance with Section 8 of the General Standard.

CODEX GENERAL GUIDELINES ON CLAIMS

CAC/GL 1-1979 (Rev. 1-1991)[1]

1.   SCOPE AND GENERAL PRINCIPLES

1.1   These guidelines relate to claims made for a food irrespective of whether or not the food is covered by an individual Codex Standard.

1.2   The principle on which the guidelines are based is that no food should be described or presented in a manner that is false, misleading or deceptive or is likely to create an erroneous impression regarding its character in any respect.

1.3   The person marketing the food should be able to justify the claims made.

2.   DEFINITION

For the purpose of these guidelines, a claim is any representation which states, suggests or implies that a food has particular characteristics relating to its origin, nutritional properties, nature, production, processing, composition or any other quality.

3.   PROHIBITED CLAIMS

The following claims should be prohibited:

3.1   Claims stating that any given food will provide an adequate source of all essential nutrients, except in the case of well defined products for which a Codex standard regulates such claims as admissible claims or where appropriate authorities have accepted the product to be an adequate source of all essential nutrients.

3.2   Claims implying that a balanced diet or ordinary foods cannot supply adequate amounts of all nutrients.

3.3   Claims which cannot be substantiated.

---

[1]   The Codex General Guidelines on Claims was adopted by the Codex Alimentarius Commission at its 13th Session, 1979. A revised version of the Codex General Guidelines on Claims was adopted by the 19th Session of the Commission in 1991. It has been sent to all Member Nations and Associate Members of FAO and WHO as an advisory text, and it is for individual governments to decide what use they wish to make of the Guidelines.

3.4   Claims as to the suitability of a food for use in the prevention, alleviation, treatment or cure of a disease, disorder, or particular physiological condition unless they are:

(a)   in accordance with the provisions of Codex standards or guidelines for foods under jurisdiction of the Committee on Foods for Special Dietary Uses and follow the principles set forth in these guidelines.

or,

(b)   in the absence of an applicable Codex standard or guideline, permitted under the laws of the country in which the food is distributed.

3.5   Claims which could give rise to doubt about the safety of similar food or which could arouse or exploit fear in the consumer.

4.   POTENTIALLY MISLEADING CLAIMS

The following are examples of claims which may be misleading:

4.1   Meaningless claims including incomplete comparatives and superlatives.

4.2   Claims as to good hygienic practice, such as "wholesome", "healthful", "sound".

5.   CONDITIONAL CLAIMS

5.1   The following claims should be permitted subject to the particular condition attached to each:

(i)   An indication that a food has obtained an increased or special nutritive value by means of the addition of nutrients, such as vitamins, minerals and amino acids may be given only if such an addition has been made on the basis of nutritional considerations according to the Codex General Principles for the Addition of Essential Nutrients to Foods. This kind of indication should be subject to legislation by the appropriate authorities.

(ii)   An indication that the food has special nutritional qualities by the reduction or omission of a nutrient should be on the basis of nutritional considerations and subject to legislation by the appropriate authorities.

(iii)   Terms such as "natural", "pure", "fresh", "home made", "organically grown" and "biologically grown" when they are used, should be in accordance with the national practices in the country where the food is sold. The use of these terms should be consistent with the prohibitions set out in Section 3.

(iv)   Religious or Ritual Preparation (e.g. Halal, Kosher) of a food may be claimed provided that the food conforms to the requirements of the appropriate religious or ritual authorities. (See also Page 47 *et seq.*).

v)   Claims that a food has special characteristics when all such foods have the same characteristics, if this fact is apparent in the claim.

(vi)   Claims which highlight the absence or non-addition of particular substances to food may be used provided that they are not misleading and provided that the substance:

> (a)   is not subject to specific requirements in any Codex Standard or Guideline;
>
> (b)   is one which consumers would normally expect to find in the food;
>
> (c)   has not been substituted by another giving the food equivalent characteristics unless the nature of the substitution is clearly stated with equal prominence; and
>
> (d)   is one whose presence or addition is permitted in the food.

(vii)   Claims which highlight the absence or non-addition of one or more nutrients should be regarded as nutrition claims and therefore should invoke mandatory nutrient declaration in accordance with the Codex Guidelines on Nutrition Labelling.

CODEX GUIDELINES ON NUTRITION LABELLING

CAC/GL 2-1985 (Rev. 1 - 1993) [1]

PURPOSE OF THE GUIDELINES

To ensure that nutrition labelling is effective:

- In providing the consumer with information about a food so that a wise choice of food can be made;

- in providing a means for conveying information of the nutrient content of a food on the label;

- in encouraging the use of sound nutrition principles in the formulation of foods which would benefit public health;

- in providing the opportunity to include supplementary nutrition information on the label.

To ensure that nutrition labelling does not describe a product or present information about it which is in any way false, misleading, deceptive or insignificant in any manner.

To ensure that no nutritional claims are made without nutrition labelling.

---

[1]   The Codex Guidelines on Nutrition Labelling were adopted by the Codex Alimentarius Commission at its 16th Session, 1985. The Nutrient Reference Values for Food Labelling Purposes in Section 3.4.4 were amended by the 20th Session of the Commission, 1993. They have been sent to all Member Nations and Associate Members of FAO and WHO as an advisory text, and it is for individual governments to decide what use they wish to make of the Guidelines.

PRINCIPLES FOR NUTRITION LABELLING

A. NUTRIENT DECLARATION

- Information supplied should be for the purpose of providing consumers with a suitable profile of nutrients contained in the food and considered to be of nutritional importance. The information should not lead consumers to believe that there is exact quantitative knowledge of what individuals should eat in order to maintain health, but rather to convey an understanding of the quantity of nutrients contained in the product. A more exact quantitative delineation for individuals is not valid because there is no meaningful way in which knowledge about individual requirements can be used in labelling.

B. SUPPLEMENTARY NUTRITION INFORMATION

- The content of supplementary nutrition information will vary from one country to another and within any country from one target population group to another according to the educational policy of the country and the needs of the target groups.

C. NUTRITION LABELLING

- Nutrition labelling should not deliberately imply that a food which carries such labelling has necessarily any nutritional advantage over a food which is not so labelled.

1. SCOPE

1.1　These guidelines recommend procedures for the nutrition labelling of foods.

1.2　These guidelines apply to the nutrition labelling of all foods. For foods for special dietary uses, more detailed provisions may be developed.

2. DEFINITIONS

For the purpose of these guidelines:

2.1　*Nutrition labelling* is a description intended to inform the consumer of nutritional properties of a food.

2.2　Nutrition labelling consists of two components:

(a)   nutrient declaration;

(b)   supplementary nutrition information.

2.3   *Nutrition declaration* means a standardized statement or listing of the nutrient content of a food.

2.4   *Nutrition claim* means any representation which states, suggests or implies that a food has particular nutritional properties including but not limited to the energy value and to the content of protein, fat and carbohydrates, as well as the content of vitamins and minerals. The following do not constitute nutrition claims:

(a)   the mention of substances in the list of ingredients;

(b)   the mention of nutrients as a mandatory part of nutrition labelling;

(c)   quantitative or qualitative declaration of certain nutrients or ingredients on the label if required by national legislation.

2.5   *Nutrient* means any substance normally consumed as a constituent of food:

(a)   which provides energy; or

(b)   which is needed for growth, development and maintenance of life; or

(c)   a deficit of which will cause characteristic bio-chemical or physiological changes to occur.

2.6   *Sugars* means all mono-saccharides and di-saccharides present in food.

2.7   *Dietary fibre* means edible plant and animal material not hydrolysed by the endogenous enzymes of the human digestive tract as determined by the agreed upon method.

2.8   *Polyunsaturated fatty acids* means fatty acids with cis-cis methylene interrupted double bonds.

3.   NUTRIENT DECLARATION

3.1   APPLICATION OF NUTRIENT DECLARATION

3.1.1 Nutrient declaration should be mandatory for foods for which nutrition claims,as defined in Section 2.4, are made.

3.1.2   Nutrient declaration should be voluntary for all other foods.

3.2   LISTING OF NUTRIENTS

3.2.1   Where nutrient declaration is applied, the declaration of the following should be mandatory:

3.2.1.1 Energy value; and

3.2.1.2 The amounts of protein, available carbohydrate (i.e., carbohydrate excluding dietary fibre) and fat; and

3.2.1.3 The amount of any other nutrient for which a nutrition claim is made; and

3.2.1.4 The amount of any other nutrient considered to be relevant for maintaining a good nutritional status, as required by national legislation.

3.2.2   Where a claim is made regarding the amount and/or the type of carbohydrate, the amount of total sugars should be listed in addition to the requirements in Section 3.2.1. The amounts of starch and/or other carbohydrate constituent(s) may also be listed. Where a claim is made regarding the dietary fibre content, the amount of dietary fibre should be declared.

3.2.3   Where a claim is made regarding the amount and/or type of fatty acids, the amounts of saturated fatty acids and of polyunsaturated fatty acids should be declared in accordance with Section 3.4.7.

3.2.4   In addition to the mandatory declaration under 3.2.1, 3.2.2 and 3.2.3, vitamins and minerals may be listed in accordance with the following criteria:

3.2.4.1 Only vitamins and minerals for which recommended intakes have been established and/or which are of nutritional importance in the country concerned should also be declared.

3.2.5   When nutrient declaration is applied, only those vitamins and minerals which are present in significant amounts should be listed.[1]

---

[1]   As a rule, 5% of the recommended intake (of the population concerned) supplied by a serving as quantified on the label should be taken into consideration in deciding what constitutes a significant amount.

3.2.6 In the case where a product is subject to labelling requirements of a Codex standard, the provisions for nutrient declaration set out in that standard should take precedence over but not conflict with the provisions of Sections 3.2.1 to 3.2.5 of these guidelines.

3.3 CALCULATION OF NUTRIENTS

3.3.1 Calculation of Energy

The amount of energy to be listed should be calculated by using the following conversion factors:

Carbohydrates	4 kcal/g - 17 kJ
Protein	4 kcal/g - 17 kJ
Fat	9 kcal/g - 37 kJ
Alcohol (Ethanol)	7 kcal/g - 29 kJ
Organic acid	3 kcal/g - 13 kJ

3.3.2 Calculation of Protein

The amount of protein to be listed should be calculated using the formula:

Protein = Total Kjeldahl Nitrogen x 6.25

unless a different factor is given in a Codex standard or in the Codex method of analysis for that food.

3.4 PRESENTATION OF NUTRIENT CONTENT

3.4.1 The declaration of nutrient content should be numerical. However, the use of additional means of presentation should not be excluded.

3.4.2 Information on energy value should be expressed in kJ and kcal per 100 g or per 100 ml or per package if the package contains only a single portion. In addition, this information may be given per serving as quantified on the label or per portion provided that the number of portions contained in the package is stated.

3.4.3 Information on the amounts of protein, carbohydrate and fat in the food should be expressed in g per 100 g or per 100 ml or per package if the package contains only a single portion. In addition, this information may be given per serving as quantified on the label or per portion provided that the number of portions contained in the package is stated.

3.4.4 Numerical information on vitamins and minerals should be expressed in metric units and/or as a percentage of the Nutrient Reference Value per 100 g or per 100 ml or per package if the package contains only a single portion. In addition, this information may be given per serving as quantified on the label or per portion provided that the number of portions contained in the package is stated.

In addition, information on protein may also be expressed as percentages of the Nutrient Reference Value.[1]

The following Nutrient Reference Values should be used for labelling purposes in the interests of international standardization and harmonization:

Protein	(g)	50
Vitamin A	(µg)	800[2]
Vitamin D	(µg)	53
Vitamin C	(mg)	60
Thiamin	(mg)	1.4
Riboflavin	(mg)	1.6
Niacin	(mg)	18[3]

---

[1]   In order to take into account future scientific developments, future FAO/WHO and other expert recommendations and other relevant information, the list of nutrients and the list of nutrient reference values should be kept under review.

[2]   Proposed addition to Section 3.2.7 (Calculation of Nutrients) of the Codex Guidelines on Nutrition Labelling: "For the declaration of β-carotene (provitamin A) the following conversion factor should be used: 1 µg retinol = 6 µg β-carotene.

[3]   Nutrient Reference Values for Vitamin D, Niacin and Iodine may not be applicable for countries where national nutrition policies or local conditions provide sufficient allowance to ensure that individual requirements are satisfied. See also section 3.2.4.1 of the Codex Guidelines on Nutrition Labelling.

Vitamin B_6	(mg)	2
Folic acid	(µg)	200
Vitamin B_{12}	(µg)	1
Calcium	(mg)	800
Magnesium	(mg)	300
Iron	(mg)	14
Zinc	(mg)	15
Iodine	(µg)	150^2
Copper	Value to be established	
Selenium	Value to be established	

3.4.5 In countries where serving sizes are normally used, the information required by Sections 3.4.2, 3.4.3 and 3.4.4 may be given per serving only as quantified on the label or per portion provided that the number of portions contained in the package is stated.

3.4.6 The presence of available carbohydrates should be declared on the label as "carbohydrates". Where the type of carbohydrate is declared, this declaration should follow immediately the declaration of the total carbohydrate content in the following format:

"Carbohydrate ... g, of which sugars ... g".

This may be followed by the following: "x" ... g

where "x" represents the specific name of any other carbohydrate constituent.

3.4.7 Where the amount and/or type of fatty acids is declared, this declaration should follow immediately the declaration of the total fat in accordance with Section 3.4.3.

The following format should be used:

Fat	... g
of which polyunsaturated	... g

and saturated   ... g

3.4   TOLERANCES AND COMPLIANCE

3.4.1   Tolerance limits should be set in relation to public health concerns, shelf-life, accuracy of analysis, processing variability and inherent lability and variability of the nutrient in the product, and, according to whether the nutrient has been added or is naturally occurring in the product.

3.4.2   The values used in nutrient declaration should be weighted average values derived from data specifically obtained from analyses of products which are representative of the product being labelled.

3.4.3   In those cases where a product is subject to a Codex standard, requirements for tolerances for nutrient declaration established by the standard should take precedence over these guidelines.

4.   *SUPPLEMENTARY NUTRITION INFORMATION*

4.1   Supplementary nutrition information is intended to increase the consumer's understanding of the nutritional value of their food and to assist in interpreting the nutrient declaration.   There are a number of ways of presenting such information that may be suitable for use on food labels.

4.2   The use of supplementary nutrition information on food labels should be optional and should only be given in addition to, and not in place of, the nutrient declaration, except for target populations who have a high illiteracy rate and/or comparatively little knowledge of nutrition.   For these, food group symbols or other pictorial or colour presentations may be used without the nutrient declaration.

4.3   Supplementary nutrition information on labels should be accompanied by consumer education programmes to increase consumer understanding and use of the information.

5.   *PERIODIC REVIEW OF NUTRITION LABELLING*

5.1   Nutrient labelling should be reviewed periodically in order to maintain the list of nutrients, to be included in composition information, up-to-date and in accord with public health facts about nutrition.

5.2   A review of optional information for nutrition education including food groups will be needed as target groups increase in literacy and nutrition knowledge.

5.3   The present definition of sugars as in Section 2.6 and that of dietary fibre as in Section 2.7 and the declaration of energy as in Section 3.4.2 should be reviewed in the light of newer developments.

GUIDELINES FOR USE OF NUTRITION CLAIMS

CAC/GL 23-1997[1]

Nutrition claims should be consistent with national nutrition policy and support that policy. Only nutrition claims that support national nutrition policy should be allowed.

1.   SCOPE

1.2   These guidelines relate to the use of nutrition claims in food labelling.

1.2   These guidelines apply to all foods for which nutrition claims are made without prejudice to specific provisions under Codex standards or Guidelines relating to Foods for Special Dietary Uses and Foods for Special Medical Purposes.

1.3   These guidelines are intended to supplement the Codex General Guidelines on Claims and do not supersede any prohibitions contained therein.

2.   DEFINITIONS

2.1   Nutrition claim[2] means any representation which states, suggests or implies that a food has particular nutritional properties including but not limited to the energy value and to the content of protein, fat and carbohydrates, as well as the content of vitamins and minerals.   The following do not constitute nutrition claims:

(a)   the mention of substances in the list of ingredients;

(b)   the mention of nutrients as a mandatory part of nutrition labelling;

---

[1]   The Codex Guidelines for the Use of Nutrtion Claims were adopted by the Codex Alimentarius Commission at its 22nd Session, 1997.   They have been sent to all Member Nations and Associate Members of FAO and WHO as an advisory text, and it is for individual governments to decide what use they wish to make of the Guidelines.

[2]   This definition is identical to the definition in the Codex Guidelines on Nutrition Labelling (CAC/GL 2-1985, Rev.1-1993).

(c)   quantitative or qualitative declaration of certain nutrients or ingredients on the label if required by national legislation.

2.1.1   *Nutrient content claim* is a nutrition claim that describes the level of a nutrient contained in a food.

(Examples:[1] "source of calcium"; "high in fibre and low in fat";)

2.1.2   *Comparative claim* is a claim that compares the nutrient levels and/or energy value of two or more foods.

(Examples: "reduced"; "less than"; "fewer"; "increased"; "more than".)

2.1.3 *Nutrient function claim* is a nutrition claim that describes the physiological role of the nutrient in growth, development and normal functions of the body.

(Examples: "Calcium aids in the development of strong bones and teeth";

                   "Protein helps build and repair body tissues";

                   "Iron is a factor in red blood cell formation";

                   Vitamin E protects the fat in body tissues from oxidation".

                   "Contains folic acid: folic acid contributes to the normal growth of the fetus."

3.   NUTRITION LABELLING

Any food for which a nutrition claim is made should be labelled with a nutrient declaration in accordance with Section 3 of the Codex Guidelines on Nutrition Labelling.

4.   NUTRITION CLAIMS

The only nutrition claims permitted shall be those relating to energy, protein, carbohydrate, and fat and components thereof, fibre, sodium and vitamins and minerals for which Nutrient Reference Values (NRVs) have been laid down in the Codex Guidelines for Nutrition Labelling.

---

[1]   Examples included for clarification of definitions.

5.   NUTRIENT CONTENT CLAIMS

5.1   When a nutrient content claim that is listed in the Table to these Guidelines or a synonymous claim is made, the conditions specified in the Table for that claim should apply.

5.2   Where a food is by its nature low in or free of the nutrient that is the subject of the claim, the term describing the level of the nutrient should not immediately precede the name of the food but should be in the form "a low (naming the nutrient) food" or "a (naming the nutrient)-free food".

6.   COMPARATIVE CLAIMS

Comparative claims should be permitted subject to the following conditions and based on the food as sold, taking into account further preparation required for consumption according to the instructions for use on the label:

6.1   The foods being compared should be different versions of the same food or similar foods. The foods being compared should be clearly identified.

6.2   A statement of the amount of difference in the energy value or nutrient content should be given. The following information should appear in close proximity to the comparative claim:

6.2.1 The amount of difference related to the same quantity, expressed as a percentage, fraction, or an absolute amount. Full details of the comparison should be given.

6.2.2 The identity of the food(s) to which the food is being compared. The food(s) should be described in such a manner that it (they) can be readily identified by consumers.

6.3   The comparison should be based on a relative difference of at least 25% in the energy value or nutrient content, except for micronutrients where a 10% difference in the NRV would be acceptable, between the compared foods and a minimum absolute difference in the energy value or nutrient content equivalent to the figure defined as "low" or as a "source" in the Table to these Guidelines[1].

6.4   The use of the word "light" should follow the same criteria as for "reduced" and include an indication of the characteristics which make the food "light".

7.   *NUTRIENT FUNCTION CLAIMS*

Claims relating to the function of a nutrient in the body should be permitted provided the following conditions are fulfilled:

7.1   Only those essential nutrients for which a Nutrient Reference Value (NRV) has been established in the Codex Guidelines on Nutrition Labelling or those nutrients which are mentioned in officially recognized dietary guidelines of the national authority having jurisdiction, should be the subject of a nutrient function claim;

7.2   The food for which the claim is made should be a significant source of the nutrient in the diet;

7.3   The nutrient function claim should be based on the scientific consensus which is supported by the competent authority.

7.4   The claim should not imply or include any statement to the effect that the nutrient would afford a cure or treatment for or protection from disease;

8.   *CLAIMS RELATED TO DIETARY GUIDELINES OR HEALTHY DIETS*

Claims that relate to dietary guidelines or "healthy diets" should be permitted subject to the following conditions:

8.1   Only claims related to the pattern of eating contained in dietary guidelines officially recognized by the appropriate national authority.

8.2   Flexibility in the wording of claims is acceptable, provided the claims remain faithful to the pattern of eating outlined in the dietary guidelines.

8.3   Claims related to a "healthy diet" or any synonymous term are considered to be claims about the pattern of eating contained in dietary guidelines and should be consistent with the guidelines.

8.4   Foods which are described as part of a healthy diet, healthy balance, etc., should not be based on selective consideration of one or more aspects of the food. They should satisfy certain minimum criteria for other major nutrients related to dietary guidelines.

8.5   Foods should not be described as "healthy" or be represented in a manner that implies that a food in and of itself will impart health.

8.6   Foods may be described as part of a "healthy diet" provided that the label carries a statement relating the food to the pattern of eating described in the dietary guidelines.

TABLE

COMPONENT	CLAIM	CONDITIONS NOT MORE THAN
Energy	Low	40 kcal (170 kJ) per 100 g (solids) or 20 kcal (80 kJ) per 100 ml (liquids)
Fat	Low	3 g per 100 g (solids)
	Free	1.5 g per 100 ml (liquids) 0.15 g per 100 g/ml
Saturated Fat	Low	1.5 g per 100 g (solids) 0.75 g per 100 g (liquids) and 10% of energy
Cholesterol	Low	20 mg per 100 g (solids) 10 mg per 100 ml (liquids) 10% of energy and less than: 1.5 g saturates per 100 g (solids) 0.75 g saturates per 100 g (liquids) and 10% of energy
Sugars	Free	0.5 g per 100 g/ml
Sodium	Low	120 mg per 100 g
	Very Low	40 mg per 100 g
	Free	5 mg per 100 g

GENERAL GUIDELINES FOR USE OF THE TERM "HALAL"

CAC/GL 24-1997[1]

The Codex Alimentarius Commission accepts that there may be minor differences in opinion in the interpretation of lawful and unlawful animals and in the slaughter act, according to the different Islamic Schools of Thought. As such, these general guidelines are subjected to the interpretation of the appropriate authorities of the importing countries. However, the certificates granted by the religious authorities of the exporting country should be accepted in principle by the importing country, except when the latter provides justification for other specific requirements.

1   SCOPE

1.1   These guidelines recommend measures to be taken on the use of Halal claims in food labelling.

1.2   These guidelines apply to the use of the term halal and equivalent terms in claims as defined in the General Standard for the Labelling of Prepackaged Foods and include its use in trade marks, brand names and business names.

1.3   These guidelines are intended to supplement the Codex General Guidelines on Claims and do not supersede any prohibition contained therein.

2   DEFINITION

2.1   Halal Food means food permitted under the Islamic Law and should fulfil the following conditions:

---

[1]   The Codex General Guidelines for the Use of the Term "Halal" were adopted by the Codex Alimentarius Commission at its 22nd Session, 1997.   They have been sent to all Member Nations and Associate Members of FAO and WHO as an advisory text, and it is for individual governments to decide what use they wish to make of the Guidelines.

2.1.1 does not consist of or contain anything which is considered to be unlawful according to Islamic Law;

2.1.2 has not been prepared, processed, transported or stored using any appliance or facility that was not free from anything unlawful according to Islamic Law; and

2.1.3 has not in the course of preparation, processing, transportation or storage been in direct contact with any food that fails to satisfy 2.1.1 and 2.1.2 above.

2.2   Notwithstanding Section 2.1 above:

2.2.1 *halal* food can be prepared, processed or stored in different sections or lines within the same premises where non-halal foods are produced, provided that necessary measures are taken to prevent any contact between halal and non-halal foods;

2.2.2 *halal* food can be prepared, processed, transported or stored using facilities which have been previously used for non-halal foods provided that proper cleaning procedures, according to Islamic requirements, have been observed.

3   CRITERIA FOR USE OF THE TERM "HALAL"

3.1   LAWFUL FOOD

The term halal may be used for foods which are considered lawful. Under the Islamic Law, all sources of food are lawful except the following sources, including their products and derivatives which are considered unlawful:

3.1.1   *Food of Animal Origin*

(a) Pigs and boars.

(b) Dogs, snakes and monkeys.

(c) Carnivorous animals with claws and fangs such as lions, tigers, bears and other similar animals.

(d) Birds of prey with claws such as eagles, vultures, and other similar birds.

(e) Pests such as rats, centipedes, scorpions and other similar animals.

(f) Animals forbidden to be killed in Islam i.e., ants, bees and woodpecker birds.

(g) Animals which are considered repulsive generally like lice, flies, maggots and other similar animals.

(h) Animals that live both on land and in water such as frogs, crocodiles and other similar animals.

(i) Mules and domestic donkeys.

(j) All poisonous and hazardous aquatic animals.

(k) Any other animals not slaughtered according to Islamic Law.

(l) Blood.

3.1.2 *Food of Plant Origin*
Intoxicating and hazardous plants except where the toxin or hazard can be eliminated during processing.

3.1.3 *Drink*
(a) Alcoholic drinks.

(b) All forms of intoxicating and hazardous drinks.

3.1.4 *Food Additives*
All food additives derived from Items 3.1.1, 3.1.2 and 3.1.3.

3.2 SLAUGHTERING
All lawful land animals should be slaughtered in compliance with the rules laid down in the Codex Recommended Code of Hygienic Practice for Fresh Meat[1] and the following requirements:

3.2.1 The person should be a Muslim who is mentally sound and knowledgeable of the Islamic slaughtering procedures.

3.2.2 The animal to be slaughtered should be lawful according to Islamic law.

---

[1]   CAC/RCP 11, Rev.1-1993.

3.2.3   The animal to be slaughtered should be alive or deemed to be alive at the time of slaughtering.

3.2.4   The phrase "Bismillah" (In the Name of Allah) should be invoked immediately before the slaughter of each animal.

3.2.5   The slaughtering device should be sharp and should not be lifted off the animal during the slaughter act.

3.2.6   The slaughter act should sever the trachea, oesophagus and main arteries and veins of the neck region.

3.3   PREPARATION, PROCESSING, PACKAGING, TRANSPORTATION AND STORAGE

All food should be prepared, processed, packaged, transported and stored in such a manner that it complies with Section 2.1 and 2.1 above and the Codex General Principles on Food Hygiene and other relevant Codex Standards.

4   ADDITIONAL LABELLING REQUIREMENTS

4.1   When a claim is made that a food is halal, the word *halal* or equivalent terms should appear on the label.

4.2   In accordance with the Codex General Guidelines on Claims, claims on halal should not be used in ways which could give rise to doubt about the safety of similar food or claims that halal foods are nutritionally superior to, or healthier than, other foods.

INDEX